# MARBLE SEASON

by GILBERT HERNANDEZ

Entire contents © 2013 by Gilbert Hernandez. All rights reserved. No part of this book (except small portions for review purposes) may be reproduced in any form without written permission from Gilbert Hernandez or Faber and Faber. "What it Feels Like: Childhood in Gilbert Hernandez's *Marble Season*" © 2013 by Corey K. Creekmur. www.faber.co.uk. First published in the United Kingdom in 2013 by Faber and Faber Limited, Bloomsbury House, 74-77 Great Russell Street, London WC1B 3DA. First published in the United States and Canada by Drawn & Quarterly, Post Office Box 48056, Montreal, Quebec, Canada H2V 4S8. Printed in Italy. The right of Gilbert Hernandez to be identified as author of this work has been asserted in accordance with Section 77 of the Copyright, Designs and Patents Act 1988. ISBN 978-0-571-30336-6. A CIP record for this book is available from the British Library. 10 9 8 7 6 5 4 3 2 1.

BETO-2012

2

3

UP ON THE ROOOF...

THAT SONG HAS A GOOD TUNE!

UP ON THE ROOF..

HEY, JUNIOR! WANT TO PLAY MARBLES?

NEH...

HUEY! THEY GAVE ME THIS FUNNYBOOK AT THE BARBER SHOP!

CHECK IT OUT!

THIS SCIENTIST HAS, LIKE, AN ELECTRONIC BRAIN STUCK ON HIS HEAD THAT LOOKS LIKE A T.V. SET, RIGHT?

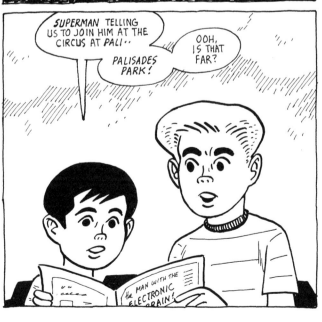

SUPERMAN TELLING US TO JOIN HIM AT THE CIRCUS AT PALI··

PALISADES PARK!

OOH, IS THAT FAR?

the MAN WITH THE ELECTRONIC BRAIN!

GO PLAY WITH YOUR MARBLES.

9

JEEPERS, SUPAMAN!

I THOUGHT THAT HE SHOT HIMSELF, BUT MAYBE HE DID JUMP OUT OF A WINDOW; I DON'T KNOW.

IT'S SUPPOSED TO COME BACK LIKE A BOOMERANG.

YEAH, LIKE *CAPTAIN AMERICA'S* SHIELD.

WHERE'S MY FRISBEE?

YEAH... IT'S ALREADY BLUE, SO I JUST HAVE TO PAINT RED AND WHITE RINGS AND A WHITE STAR IN THE MIDDLE, JUST LIKE *CAP'S* SHIELD.

THAT PAINT IS FOR MODEL KITS; IT WON'T STICK.

YEAH IT WILL.

HEY, LET ME PUT A WIRE ACROSS THE INSIDE SO YOUR FOREARM CAN HOLD IT, JUST LIKE *CAP.*

HEY, YEAH.

PUNCH HOLES INTO THE OPPOSITE ENDS...

IT'S GONNA BE COOL, HUH, CHAVO?

21

25

27

29

CLICK...

NOBODY'S AS FUNNY AS JIMMY OLSEN.

EXCEPT FOR CURLY AND JERRY LEWIS.

AND GRANNY.

HERE, CHAVO. LET ME SHOW YOU HOW TO UNDERSTAND COMIC BOOKS.

OK, HERE'S A COMIC ABOUT A SUPER TEAM THAT ARE KIND OF LIKE MONSTERS.

THIS GUY HERE WHO LOOKS THE MOST LIKE A MONSTER IS ACTUALLY A GOOD GUY.

THE THING!

NOW, THE HULK'S A MONSTER TOO, OK, BUT IT'S HARD TO TELL IF HE'S GOOD OR BAD, OK?

NOBODY CAN TELL!

HEY, MAKE SURE CHAVO DOESN'T TEAR UP THAT COMIC OR I'LL TEAR YOU UP, HUEY.

THEY ALWAYS HAVE MUSCLE MAN ADVERTISEMENTS IN COMICS, HUH?

WE USED TO CALL THESE FUNNYBOOKS, BUT NOW WE CALL THEM COMIC BOOKS, OR JUST COMICS.

43

I'M LOOKING THROUGH OUR COMICS THAT HAVE DIFFERENT MUSCLE MAN ADVERTISEMENTS.

IF I POSE LIKE THE GUY DOING THIS, I'LL GET MUSCLES TOO.

WHAT'RE YOU DOING NOW?

EXERCISING!

OK, CHAYO, US TOO!

THIS IS MY FAVORITE COMIC ABOUT GOOD GUYS THAT ARE MONSTERS.

THE DOOM PATROL.

ALTHOUGH ELASTI-GIRL'S NO MONSTER, THAT'S FOR SURE.

44

51

53

59

71

84

85

The End

# What it Feels Like: Childhood in Gilbert Hernandez's Marble Season
## Corey K. Creekmur

Every year, it seems, yet another clueless journalist writes yet another irrelevant article with the "breaking news" that "comics aren't just for kids anymore!" But does anyone still not know this? A half-century after R. Crumb's Zap Comix ("Fair Warning: For Adult Intellectuals Only!") relocated comics within a counter-cultural underground, or a quarter-century after Maus, Art Spiegelman's holocaust memoir in the form of a "funny animal comic," won a Pulitzer Prize, this is news? Ignoring the historical fact that adults have always read comics, many other touchstones might be invoked to mark the unofficial maturation of comics, but I'll choose just one. The ban on those tedious and culturally oblivious announcements should have immediately followed the 1981 appearance of the first issue of the comic book Love and Rockets by the artists who identified themselves as "Los Bros Hernandez." One of the defining (and, remarkably, lasting) examples of the post-underground, alternative comics renaissance of the 1980s, the black-and-white, magazine-sized Love and Rockets should have made it impossible for anyone to ever again dismiss comics, simply because they were comics, as merely "kid's stuff."

While they often drew upon childish -- or at least adolescent – source material in their comics, Gilbert and Jaime Hernandez, the main "bros" behind Love and Rockets, almost immediately combined the "adult" aspect of many earlier underground comix (in a word, sex) with an almost unprecedented artistic and narrative sophistication that demanded (and rewarded) mature readers who felt they had outgrown comic books. Indeed, in their wake -- and following the emergence of key figures like Chris Ware, Joe Sacco, Alison Bechdel, and many others whose work could hardly be mistaken for children's literature -- the real story persistently missed by those out-of-touch journalists is that, with rare exceptions, very few comics are for kids anymore. Once a genuine form of mass culture consumed by a large number of male and female children as well as adults, comics now address a narrowing niche market, a largely male subculture getting older all the time. Millions of people viewing recent big-budget superhero films

no longer read the comics these are based on, in part because the convoluted continuities established by mainstream comic publishers haven't welcomed new readers for decades. While the recent legitimation of some comics as "graphic novels" has encouraged many readers who "don't read comics" to, well, read comics, these are largely marketed to hip adult consumers with disposable incomes, not to kids who don't yet view comics as edgy art or as investments to be sealed in plastic. On the whole, reading comics (except perhaps for the curious case of manga) is less and less a common experience of contemporary childhood. And, again, among those who effectively redirected comics away from their artistically limiting association with children were Gilbert and Jaime Hernandez, whose early work secured an especially devoted following among older readers, including the young women who by then had been virtually abandoned as an audience by mainstream American publishers.

Love and Rockets was actually the creation of three young men: Gilbert, who often signs his work as Beto, his younger brother Jaime (or Xaime), and their older brother Mario, whose contributions to the comic have been significant but less frequent. While a genuine family project as a whole, within its issues (fifty between 1982 and 1996, and ongoing in different incarnations) the comic typically divides into two ambitious, long-running, richly populated narratives. Gilbert's stories are set in the mythic Latin American town of Palomar, and often center around his formidable heroine Luba, while Jaime's stories largely take place in the Southern California barrio called Hoppers and feature the group of young women he calls "Locas," most famously the beloved (former) punk rockers Maggie and Hopey. Although both Gilbert and Jaime have written funny or sweet stories, as noted, their work often explores what are typically characterized as "adult" themes, including the vagaries of human desire and (shall we say) earthy sexuality, as well as traumatic acts of violence and social injustice that too often define the culturally diverse societies their multi-ethnic and class-divided characters inhabit.

But amidst the remarkable, decades-long unfolding of these continuing sagas, the amazingly prolific Gilbert has also created works for kids, including the wacky series Yeah! (1999-2000, collected 2011), written by fellow cartoonist Peter Bagge, about an all-girl intergalactic rock band, and most recently The Adventures of Venus (2012), a series of short pieces about the exploits of a spunky girl soccer player (and budding cartoonist). Marble Season in some ways extends these works, while shifting the focus from girls to boys, and also continues the artist's steady creation of additional graphic novels apart from the Palomar stories beginning with Sloth (2006) and continuing with Speak of the Devil (2008) and (with brother Mario) Citizen Rex (2009, collected 2011). Marble Season is thus linked in different ways to Gilbert's larger body of work but also signals a subtle new focus: while children have appeared throughout his work, and in a few cases been his intended audience, now the experience of childhood itself seems to be his concern. (One sign of this shift is that, unlike his own previous work, but in the tradition of many previous kids' comics, Marble Season is set in a virtually all-kids world, with parents and teachers kept just off-stage. Parents and teachers exist in this world, but they aren't very relevant to it.)

Certainly kids have always been prominent in the work of both Hernandez brothers, even when that work hasn't been appropriate for kids. Jaime has drawn both charming and harrowing flashbacks of his main characters as children, and the sheer vital energy of kids has always been a major part of the multigenerational world of Gilbert's Palomar, and of the matriarchal Luba's life beyond Palomar in America. In addition to their regular roles within those ongoing narratives, children in Love and Rockets also extend the long legacy of kids in comics from Winsor McCay's dreaming Little Nemo forward. This is not just a question of shared content: if one finds echoes of the pint-sized worlds of Charles M. Schulz's Peanuts or John Stanley's Little Lulu (with its infamous "no girls allowed" boys' club invoked in Marble Season) within Gilbert's and Jaime's stories, their remarkably expressive drawings of little kids also acknowledge the notable stylistic influences of Hank Ketcham's Dennis the Menace (actually drawn for comic books by ghost artist Owen Fitzgerald) and Bob Bolling's

Little Archie comics. (I have always found Gilbert and Jaime's ready willingness to acknowledge emphatically unhip comics among their major inspirations to be both honest and charming.)

However, even as they echo and pay homage to such models, kids in the Hernandez brothers' work do not inhabit the nostalgic, insulated and often all-white world of most earlier comics. At times their children are witnesses to and even perpetrators of savage cruelty: they can also be, like real kids, remarkably resilient in the face of horror or deprivation. Perhaps no other current creators of comics recognize (or vividly remember) the ways actual kids think, talk, or even stand and walk as accurately as the Hernandez brothers, and no other comics artists so delicately intertwine moments of childhood trauma with the goofy logic that otherwise sustains kids when they begin to sense that they live in an irrational world. (Lynda Barry may be their only equal in this regard.) Kids in their comics are neither sentimentalized nor sappily "innocent," and thus, as in life, they can be both scary and scared, as Marble Season recognizes in its brief moments depicting bullying or hints of uncertain sexuality. They are also inspiringly imaginative when they tap into that playful, adaptable ability to ignore or overcome the rational limitations adults come to sadly impose upon themselves. Marble Season is about, among other things, the way kids -- and perhaps artists, or perhaps especially kids who become artists -- think.

My claim that Marble Season doesn't just depict but is in some sense "about" childhood may also suggest that it's simultaneously not about much and about a whole lot. At first glance, there are very few "major events" in the story (just read Gilbert's other work if you want to see how well he can stage these when he wants to) Instead, the story is made up of the seemingly minor childhood events that might take hold as lifelong memories. (Gilbert's Palomar stories have often been compared to the "magical realist" novels of Gabriel García Márquez but I'll risk pretentiousness here and label him a vato Proust as well.) Perhaps saying that Marble Season is "about" childhood misleadingly indicates a sociological study rather than a story, but instead of either exactly, I think what Gilbert offers us in this quietly powerful work is a version of what the British cultural critic

Raymond Williams famously called a "structure of feeling," a representation of the way life is lived, even or especially in the moments we might disregard as simply ordinary or everyday, within the context of a particular time and place. The focus here is therefore less on what childhood means than on what it feels like. Reading Marble Season induces those of us who are no longer children to remember that time in our own lives, less for its extraordinary highlights than to recover the once-common rhythms of childhood experience that are at greater risk of being forgotten. Based upon its many precise references to American popular culture, the story is set in the early 1960s, but it not only recalls, for all its readers, the past (the historical period when the story is set), but recreates that time as a present tense experience (the time the characters live in), while often quietly pointing towards the future (which is, of course, now, the time of the story's creation and our reading of it). We are motivated to simultaneously wonder what will become and what has become -- in the gap between their time and ours – of Huey, his brothers, and his friends. Despite its clear, linear organization, Marble Season is a kind of time travel story.

Put another way, this story centers less on the series of events it narrates than the transitions (seen and not seen) between them. From the start, Marble Season follows the nearly imperceptible mutations between, for instance, a group dynamic in which a bully can suddenly become a quaking coward as soon as someone new enters the scene; it traces the invisible line that leads from little kids who tear up comic books to kids who read and even (someday) make comics. For what it's worth, the unstable world recreated here is much closer to my own childhood than anything I ever found in the seemingly frozen worlds of an Archie or Little Lulu comic, which were nevertheless fascinating to me precisely because they depicted kids' lives so different from my own. I never hung out in an apparently eternal Chock'lit Shoppe (whatever that was) like Archie and the gang, but I did try to destroy my G. I. Joe, seeking like Gilbert's characters to figure out just how a boy was supposed to play with dolls, which might be by destroying them.

Unsurprisingly, this book's title is carefully chosen. Unlike other defined temporal markers such as days, months, or years, the perceptual borders between seasons can be imprecise and vague, and their incremental transformations hard to isolate. They are also, of course, natural transitions, like the slow but dramatic physical changes of adolescent bodies, even if we try to impose cultural order and meaning upon them (as if all thirteen-year-olds are immediately teenagers on their birthdays or as if the "first day of Spring" will determine that day's weather). "Marble season" is even less clearly defined than, say, "baseball season" (which has an official first day) and these imprecise, vague borders are what this work seeks to get on paper, even if that paper is ironically organized by a rigid series of bordered squares. Marble Season is not just a comic, like most, that signifies spatial and temporal transitions between what are in fact static panels, but it is unusually invested in the negotiation and depiction of all kinds of transitions themselves, ranging from the way a kid processes the sudden arrival and departure of new kids in the neighborhood, to the way a young boy considers his own changing body when he identifies with the mutating bodies of superheroes like the Hulk and scans the bodybuilding ads in comics, or only halfway comprehends the curious changes within a community (and in his own feelings) when the local tomboy is transformed by wearing a dress. Marble Season renders temporality in the way it is experienced by kids, or as it functions in our blurry memories of childhood, and this temporal flow rather than precise chronology is persistently manifested in the often elusive and elliptical transitions between the otherwise regular grid (six per page) of panels Gilbert employs to structure the comic itself. (This technique isn't altogether new -- both Hernandez brothers are widely considered masters of comics panel transitions – but seems especially important here as a means to intertwine form and content.)

I urge readers – if that's the right word here – to linger on rather than speed past the silent panels that regularly punctuate this story. They aren't simple filler, but serve as their own little time capsules, moments for us as well as Gilbert's characters to pause, reflect, and take breath before moving forward. They are what the philosopher William James called "felt time" looks and feels like in comics. They represent change that, at the time, doesn't feel like change, or at least like significant or momentous change, but which looks incredibly precious when it has passed, in retrospect.

If Marble Season encourages us to time travel by recalling and appreciating subtle change as we remember our own childhoods while we proceed – slowly, I hope -- from panel to panel, it also makes a case for the affective value of the icons and objects of American mass culture in that process. While there's no question that one of the major contributions of the Hernandez brothers to the history of American comics is their rich representation of multiethnic and multiracial communities, I sometimes think a bit too much has been made of this innovation. Despite the racial and ethnic differences that begin (as shown here) to ground the identities of young men and may eventually work to isolate them from one another, Gilbert's kids otherwise share an immersion in American mass culture. The dozens of allusions to songs, TV shows, movies, toys, and other commercial products (yeah, comics too) throughout Marble Season function as the lingua franca of childhood that allows difference to be overcome through a shared vocabulary and effective translations. The comics of the Hernandez brothers have always been densely and playfully allusive, but the many citations of popular culture in Marble Season seem less like hip, subcultural signifiers to reward insiders (as they often could be in Love and Rockets) than a catalog of the once-familiar items that would be the result of an archeological excavation of America in the early 1960s: this is the stuff you would uncover if you dug up a buried school playground or a boy's bedroom from the era. Sure, this is the ephemeral detritus of junk culture, meant to be played with until broken and discarded, or fated to be tossed out by your mother with the rest of the trash: but, as kids all know, these lowly objects might also function as magical fetishes and sacred totems, bits of fragile paper and plastic that nevertheless once sparked the imagination and now give material weight and concrete detail to otherwise elusive memories. Perhaps no one except Gilbert Hernandez vividly recalls the obscure comic book story "The Man with the Electronic Brain," written by Gardner Fox and drawn by Murphy Anderson, which appeared in DC's Strange Adventures #128 in May 1961: but Huey, at least, appreciates the story's

clever gimmick, and retains the encouraging lesson (your brain can be your superpower!) it entertainingly conveyed. Mass culture, in its sheer massiveness, works that way: some of it, like the new pop group these kids call "The Beatos," attracts a vast audience and obtains lasting value, whereas some of it may only ever resonate with one or two people, or within a few neighborhoods. Huey has been collecting the infamous Topps trading-card set Mars Attacks, which told the grisly story of Earth's near-destruction before finally blowing up Mars. Even though they were "stacked all nice and neat," his mother "just saw them as trash" and casually tosses them out. The card sets are now rare and valuable collector's items precisely because that's what happened to most of them, but Marble Season indicates that although as objects these and other treasures disappear from Huey's life, those cheap and lurid products of American mass culture – just kids' stuff, after all – nevertheless retain their impact, perhaps for decades. If you managed (as few did) to collect all fifty-five cards in the set, they told a linked story, not so different in structure from a series of sequential comics panels, and even though each card depicted a somewhat isolated incident, they could be "stacked all nice and neat" rather like the pages you encounter in Marble Season itself.

The rising status and value (literal and symbolic) of the artifacts of 1960s commercial culture is another curious transformation Marble Season hints at, and Huey's suspicion that the only thing he "knows how to do right is read comic books" sadly discredits his own already vivid story-creating imagination by affirming the dominant values of his society. From our critical distance, we might suspect that, like his creator, Huey might some day put that unrecognized talent to good use. (There's good reason to read this work as semi-autobiographical, despite the changed names of Gilbert's characters: at the same time, it's worth noting that Gilbert Hernandez grew up with four brothers, and one sister, so creative license may also be allowed in this work about the creative imagination.) All Huey will have to do is remember and -- the far more difficult task -- continue to value the magic word he casually yet defiantly invokes whenever his "childish" fantasies are questioned: "pretend."

There are numerous pop culture references that may be lost on some moderns readers. Gilbert Hernandez has chosen to detail these references for our edification.

**Page 3**, *panel 4:* The war that Huey refers to is World War Two.

**Page 5**, *panel 1:* "Up on the Roof" is a song by The Drifters. It reached #5 on the US pop charts in 1962.
   *panel 3:* The comic Junior is holding is Strange Adventures #128 (DC Comics).
   *panel 5:* Palisades Park was an East Coast (Bergen County, New Jersey) amusement park that eventually closed in 1971.

**Page 12**, *panel 3:* Bozo the Clown was an American children's TV show whose popularity peaked in the 1960s.
   *panel 4:* Jimmy Olsen is a character in the Superman series, played by Jack Larson in Adventures of Superman 1950s TV show.

**Page 13**   panel 1: Lana is referring to a myth that George Reeves, the actor who played Superman in the TV series Adventures of Superman, mistakenly thought that he had acquired Superman's power of flight and jumped out of a window to his death. In reality, Reeves died of a gunshot wound on June 16, 1959.

Page 16, panel 1: Red Skull was the name borne by several Marvel villains. The first two Red Skulls were Nazis and enemies of Captain America, while the third Red Skull—famous for killing Peter Parker's parents—was a Soviet and faced off against the Grand Director (a hero who impersonated Captain America after his disappearance in 1945).

Page 17, panel 2: Carbon paper is coated on one side with a pigment that transfers to a piece of paper underneath when pressure is applied, allowing multiple copies of a document to be written at once.

Page 20, panel 6: It's a Mad, Mad, Mad World is a 1963 comedy film starring many of the greatest comedians of the day, including Mickey Rooney, Ethel Merman, and Phil Silvers.

Page 28, panel 5: The comic Huey is holding is The Incredible Hulk #2 (Marvel Comics).

Page 37, panel 2: Curly Howard was a slapstick comedian, best known for being one of The Three Stooges. Jerry Lewis was a Hollywood comedian who originally performed as a team with Dean Martin. The duo was so popular that they had their own DC Comics series and after they went their separate ways, the DC comic continued with Jerry Lewis in solo adventures. Granny is a character from the 1960s TV comedy The Beverly Hillbillies, played by Irene Ryan.

   panel 2: The comic Chavo is holding is the Fantastic Four (Marvel Comics).

Page 39, panels 5-6: Huey is singing the theme song from The Mighty Hercules TV cartoon series (1963-1966).

Page 43, panels 1-2: "Thank You, Girl" is a song by the Beatles. It reached #35 on the US pop charts in 1964.

   panel 5: Mike Nelson is the lead character in Sea Hunt, a TV show that aired from 1958-1961. He was played by Lloyd Bridges.

Page 44, panel 6: Elasti-Girl can grow into a giant or shrink down to the size of a mouse, and wears a very short skirt. The Doom Patrol was a superhero team created by DC Comics that first appeared in 1963.

Page 46, panel 3: Mars Attacks was a set of trading cards created by Topps in 1962.
Page 49, panel 5: Mr. Sardonicus was a 1960s horror film whose

protagonist's face had been frozen into a horrifying grin while digging up his father's grave for a winning lottery ticket.

Page 57, panel 2: "You've Lost that Lovin' Feeling'" is a song by The Righteous Brothers. It was number one on US and UK charts in 1965.

   panel 6: Lucio is singing the Hasbro jingle used in the 1960s for their G.I. Joe toy line. The tune is based on "The Army Goes Rolling Along," the official song of the US Army.

Page 57, panel 2: "She Loves You" is a song by The Beatles. It was number one on US and UK charts in 1964.

Page 60, panel 4: The Dick Tracy Show always opened with the title character calling one of his associates with his two-way wrist radio to assign them a case. Go Go Gomez, one of these assistants, was a stereotyped Mexican who wore a sombrero.

Page 62, panels 5-6: "You Can't Hurry Love" is a song by The Supremes that topped US charts in 1966.

Page 63, panel 1: The comic that Huey is given is Ghost Stories #1 (Dell Comics).

Page 70, panels 1-2: Birdman's battle cry from 1960's TV cartoon series Birdman and the Galaxy Trio.
   panel 6: Project Mercury was the US's first human spaceflight program and ran from 1959 to 1963.

Page 90, panel 3: Buddy Austin and Mark Lewen were American heavyweight wrestlers. Austin debuted in the early 1960s and Lewen in the early 1950s.
   panel 4: Shindig! was a variety show that aired in the 1960s, hosted by Jimmy O'Neill.
   panel 5: Dick Lane was a television announcer for wrestling and roller derby on the Los Angeles channel KTLA.

Page 93, panel 5: Creepy was a horror magazine published by Warren Publishing. Mad was an independent satirical magazine founded by Harvey Kurtzman and William Gaines. Both magazines avoided the Comics Code Authority rules by publishing in a format they didn't regulate.

Page 101, panel 5: The Howling Commandos were characters in the Marvel Universe, led by Nick Fury.

Page 102, panel 2: The original Captain Marvel was originally published by Fawcett Comics in the 1940s. This was the 2nd character to use the name.

Page 107, panel 5: Dennis the Menace comic books were published by Fawcett Comics from 1958-1980.

Page 110, panel 3: The Hideous Sun-Demon was a 1959 film directed by Robert Clarke. It tells the story of a scientist who is exposed to radiation in his lab and then changed into a scaled demon by the sun.
panel 5: Cinderella was released by Disney in 1950.

Page 114, panel 6: Bobbie Jo was a character from the 1960's TV comedy Petticoat Junction, a companion show to The Beverly Hillbillies. She was played by Pat Woodell from 1963 to 1965 and by Lori Saunders from 1965 to 1970.

Page 115, panels 3-4: Officer Gunther Toody was a character on the sitcom Car 45, Where Are You? that aired in the 1960s and early 1070s. Toody was played by vaudeville comedian Joe E. Ross who used his characteristic "Ooh! Ooh!" exclamation in more than one role.

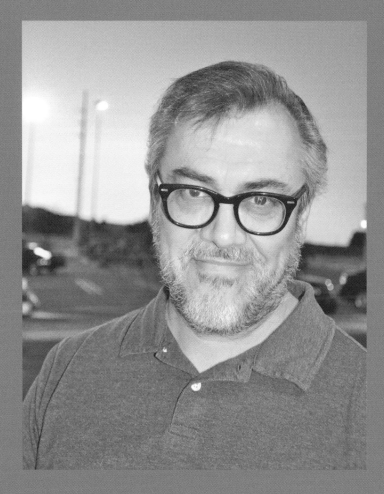

**GILBERT HERNANDEZ** was born in 1957 in Oxnard, California. In 1981, he co-self-published the first issue of *Love & Rockets* with his older brother, Mario and younger brother, Jaime. Embracing strong female lead characters and punk rock culture, this series stood out from the male dominated comics landscape of the late 1970s and early 1980s. The following year, *Love & Rockets* was picked up and republished and continued as a series by Fantagraphics Books. Gilbert Hernandez and his brother Jaime have continued *Love & Rockets* for three decades; the series is acknowledged as the creative flashpoint for the second wave of underground comics. In the ensuing years, Hernandez has been nominated for—and won—nearly every industry award, as well as the prestigious United States Artists Literature Fellowship. Hernandez currently lives in Las Vegas, Nevada with his wife, Carol, and his daughter, Natalia.